STONE AGE
NURSERY
RHYMES

Little Miss Muffet

Little Miss Muffet
Sat on a tuffet,
Eating her curds and whey.

Along came a spider
Who sat down beside her,
And frightened Miss Muffet away.

Hey Diddle, Diddle

Hey, diddle, diddle,
The cat and the fiddle,
The cow jumped over the moon;
The little dog laughed
To see such sport,
And the dish ran away
With the spoon.

Humpty Dumpty

Humpty Dumpty sat on a wall,
Humpty Dumpty had a great fall.
All the king's horses,
And all the king's men,
Couldn't put Humpty together again.

Jack Be Nimble

Jack be nimble,
Jack be quick,
Jack jump over
The candlestick!

Little Bo-Peep

Little Bo-Peep has lost her sheep,
And can't tell where to find them;
Leave them alone,
And they'll come home,
Wagging their tails behind them.

Little Boy Blue

Little Boy Blue,
Come blow your horn!
The sheep are in the meadow,
The cow is in the corn.
Where is the boy who looks
After the sheep?
He's under the haystack, fast asleep!

Sing a Song of Sixpence

Sing a song of sixpence,
A pocket full of rye,
Four and twenty blackbirds
Baked in a pie!

When the pie was opened,
The birds began to sing,
And wasn't that a dainty dish
To set before the king?

Mary, Mary Quite Contrary

Mary, Mary, quite contrary,
How does your garden grow?
With silver bells and cockle shells,
And pretty maids all in a row.

Georgy Porgy

Georgy Porgy pudding and pie,
Kissed the girls and made them cry.
When the boys came out to play,
Georgy Porgy ran away.

Old King Cole

Old King Cole was a merry old soul,
And a merry old soul was he.
He called for his pipe,
He called for his bowl,
And he called for his fiddlers three!

Rub-A-Dub-Dub

Rub-A-Dub-Dub,
Three men in a tub.
And who do you think they be?
The butcher, the baker,
The candlestick maker,
Terrible fools, all three.

Jack Sprat

Jack Sprat could eat no fat,
His wife could eat no lean.
Between them both,
They cleared the plate,
And licked the platter clean.